M000106102

POGO

by

Walt Kelly

POGO

by

Walt Kelly

FANTAGRAPHICS BOOKS

FANTAGRAPHICS BOOKS

7563 Lake City Way NE
Seattle WA 98115
Edited by Rebecca Bowen and Pat Moriarity
Designed by Pat Moriarity
Production by Adam Glickman
Published by Gary Groth and Kim Thompson

Thanks to Bill Blackbeard, Rick Norwood and Steve Thompson for historical and archival assistance.
Some original proof material provided by The Pogo Fan Club. For further information about the PFC
and their magazine, *The Fort Mudge Most*, write them at 6908 Wentworth, Richfield MN 55423.

This edition is © 1995 Fantagraphics Books; *Pogo* and all the strips in this volume are © 1995 Selby Kelly. All rights reserved.
Permission to quote or reproduce material for reviews or notices must be obtained from Fantagraphics Books, Inc.,
in writing, at 7563 Lake City Way NE, Seattle WA 98115.

First Fantagraphics Books edition: March, 1995.

10 9 8 7 6 5 4 3 2 1

ISBN: 1-56097-168-1

Printed in the U.S.A.

Only Minor Scathing: The Disney Influence

By R. C. Harvey

Harry Truman met Joseph Stalin for the first time at Potsdam in July 1945. World War II was fizzling out. It was over in Europe; Germany had surrendered in May. In the Pacific, the Allies were girding their martial loins for an invasion of the home islands of the Japanese Empire. In New Mexico and Washington, D.C., scientists and politicians were speculating about the effect on Japanese resolve of dropping a new bomb, the atomic bomb, on a couple of cities. At Potsdam, the Allies met to discuss how they would divide the spoils of the War in Europe.

Nobody trusted Stalin. The Russians had been viewed with suspicion ever since the communists came into power a generation ago. Their motives were suspect. But Russia was one of "the Big Three," allied with Britain and the United States to defeat Hitler and, eventually, Japan at the other end of the continent. Stalin had brought Russia into the western alliance because, at the time, he needed help keeping the invading armies of Hitler at bay. Now that the War was over, Stalin turned a greedy eye upon the conquered countries along his western border. These he wanted to bring into the communist fold.

Truman knew all this about Stalin, but he clung to a hope that the Russian dictator would prove, upon acquaintance, to be a reasonable man. Truman was quickly disabused of this notion. He returned from Potsdam convinced that the Russians were "planning world conquest."

The Russian ambition to subdue and convert the entire world was an article of communist faith. It made

Americans leery of communists. Although many Americans had flirted with communism in the abject years of forlorn hope during the Great Depression in the thirties, most Americans imagined communists, when they

thought about them at all, as bearded Bolsheviks, irresponsible bomb-throwers who would destroy the American Way of Life. And as they saw Stalin gobbling up the war-torn countries in Eastern Europe, their fears about communism's appetite were revived. And they were soon confirmed.

In 1946, Winston Churchill, Britain's great warhorse, gave a speech in Fulton, Missouri, in which he proclaimed the success, so far, of Russian ambition when he said that an "iron curtain" had fallen across Eastern Europe, separating the continental countries into communist and non-communist regimes. The same year, Stalin addressed a huge rally of communist party work-

ers in Russian, denouncing the possibility of coexistence with democracies and vowing to foster communist revolution wherever possible. Confronted with this kind of evidence, Americans knew communism was something to be wary of. To combat it, Truman announced "the Truman Doctrine," a policy aimed at "containing" communism, stemming its future expansion by confining it to the countries where it presently held sway.

"The Red Scare," a nearly irrational fear of anything labeled "communist" in the post-WWII years, lurked everywhere in American life. But Americans comforted themselves with the knowledge that the United States was the only country with the atom bomb. There was security in that. Then in 1949, both the foundations upon which Americans erected their teetering sense of security crumbled.

When mainland China had succumbed to Mao Tse-tung's communist forces in May, the policy of containment was seen as seriously flawed. Where would a communist regime pop up next? Then in August, it was discovered that Russia had the atomic bomb. The United States was no longer the only atomic power. Even worse, the other nuclear nation was an avowed foe.

To fan the flames of fear, the Republicans raised a great hue and cry. They had been denied the White House for nearly twenty years and now saw an opportunity to so discredit the Truman administration and the Democrats as to win the Presidency the next time out (in 1952). They accused the Democrats of "losing China." And they also suggested that the Democrats had permitted communist spies to be employed in the State Department, beady-eyed would-be Bolsheviks who had doubtless sold the secret of the atomic bomb to the Russians. In Alger Hiss, a Roosevelt New Dealer, they found their scapegoat. His first trial as a spy ended with a hung jury in May 1949; but in a second trial, he was convicted of perjury in January 1950. The Republicans had a field day. They rattled closet doors and fulminated far and wide about communists in government.

Their ranting proved, at last, too much for Walt Kelly to resist. His comic strip *Pogo* had not yet celebrated its first anniversary as a nationally syndicated feature, and Kelly, like all syndicated cartoonists of the day, avoided political commentary in his strip. Politics and syndicated comics just didn't mix. One could never be sure of the political convictions of the editors of the papers who subscribed to the strip. If the editors disagreed with something the cartoonist said in his strip, the editors would simply drop the strip. And the cartoonist's income would drop as he lost papers. Consequently, nationally syndicated cartoonists did not take political stands.

Kelly would eventually throw such caution to the winds. At present, however, he followed the customs of his craft. Mostly. But the hysterical tone of public discourse on the question of atomic secrets undoubtedly struck him as ludicrous in the extreme. In the wake of the Hiss verdict, Kelly devoted most of March's strips to Owl's researches into the secrets of the atom. Owl's moronic grasp of nuclear physics is highly comical but scarcely pointed satire. His fear of "foreign powers," however, is extreme enough to ridicule those who trembled in the grip of the Red Scare. And on March 30, Owl falls into the sight-gag snare Kelly has been building towards for several days: he sees a communist anywhere he sees a hammer and sickle, even if he provided the hammer himself and the sickle is but a sample of the skill of the neighborhood scissors grinder. (Albert in phony whiskers is obviously the fearsome bearded Bolshevik; but the beard, remember, is false. So, perhaps, are some of the alarums raised by rabid Republicans.)

Kelly's first foray into political commentary in the spring of 1949 was more good-natured kidding than hard-hitting satire. The antics of his animals for most of that year owed more to vaudeville than to Capital

Hill. And for much of his skill at his craft generally, Kelly was indebted to the Walt Disney Studios. Milton Caniff once observed in my hearing (as he doubtless had done with countless other auditors) that Walt Kelly was the only syndicated cartoonist to come out of the Mouse Factory unscathed: Kelly, Caniff said, practiced cartooning in his own fashion, unmarred by any vestige of the Disney version. I agree that Kelly's work owes no obvious debt to Disney, but the influence of Kelly's years at the Studio can be discerned nonetheless.

When Walt Kelly started to work at the Disney Studio in 1936, he worked first as a sketch artist and storyman, doing only a little animation. After several years of this, he asked Disney to be transferred to the animation department, saying he wanted to know more about animation in order to write better for the medium. Accordingly, at the end of 1939, he joined Fred Moore's unit as a junior animator. During the eighteen months that remained of his tenure at the Studio, Kelly would learn to animate the Disney way. And he would become fast friends with Ward Kimball, the senior animator in Moore's unit (destined to be christened one of the "Nine Old Men," the animators whose genius guided the Disney product for three decades or more).

A few months after Kelly joined Moore and Kimball, the Mouse Factory moved from its original home, a jerry-built conglomeration of old buildings and fresh plywood on Hyperion Boulevard, to luxurious new quarters in Burbank. (Although the Studio's new home was ostensibly designed for the production of animated films, the six-story, eight-wing complex could be converted to a hospital overnight. Hitler had invaded Poland in September 1939, and the Bank of America, which financed the building of the new studio, was hedging its bet: if Disney's burgeoning empire collapsed with the evaporation of its European market, the buildings could be sold to the government with the inevitable entry of the U.S. into the war.) In their new digs, Kimball and Kelly occupied rooms on either side of Moore's office, and connecting doorways made it easy for the three to pass back and forth from one office to another as they worked together on the projects assigned to the unit. Kimball and Kelly hit it off almost at once. They both played the tin whistle (or "six-hole flageolet," as Kimball called it) and the harmonica. In an interview with Thomas Andrae and Geoffrey Blum published in *Phi Beta Pogo* by Bill Crouch and Selby Kelly

in 1989 (Fireside), Kimball described the musical antics perpetrated by the duo:

> Our favorite pastime was when he and I would make our early morning trip to the men's john. When he felt the urge, he would stop by my room, tin whistle in hand, and ask, "Ready?" And my reply was always, "Ready!" I'd grab my tin whistle, and we'd walk to the room at the end of the hall and occupy the only two adjoining stalls. We'd sit down and play duets. We loved that men's room because it was lined with tile, which gave our musical renditions Carnegie Hall reverberations. We'd play things like "Alabammy Bound" and "Tuck Me to Sleep in My Old Kentucky Home." Kelly loved all those Southern tunes. Even though he was very East Coast... he was enamored of the South and its music, with that "you-all" syndrome.
>
> Well, we'd play these tunes, and if he was real knocked out with any of our improvisations, he'd yell, "Eatin' peanuts by the peck!" That meant it was real good. And we'd laugh like hell. Other guys would come in wanting to use the johns and plead, "All right, you guys, get your asses out and give somebody else a chance." After a concert, we'd pack up and go back to my room or go to Fred's and try out some of the tunes on him. We'd say, "Listen to this, Fred." And he'd say, "Oh, Jesus, do I have to?" Sometimes I would play drums on the wastepaper basket, or Kelly would play rhythm. We also played a zither. It was a terrible sound, but we enjoyed it for the humor involved (pp. 136-37).

Kelly loved Dixieland jazz, Kimball said — "that old-time band sound."

During the noon hours, many of the Disney employees took to the playing field outside for games of volleyball, touch football, and the like. Kimball was a good volleyball player, according to Shamus Culhane (in his autobiography, *Talking Animals and Other People*; St. Martin's Press, 1986):

> Ward Kimball was probably the shortest man on the court, but his agility made him an exceptionally good player. He was also a kind of studio pixie, given to practical jokes. Sometimes, at the height of the volley, he would perform very well, then suddenly take the ball that was hit to him and hold it lazily in his hands, drop it to the ground, and walk off with a

mischievous grin as the other devotees of the game danced with rage (p. 145).

One time as a prank, Kimball drove his car onto the volleyball court when he saw that the intensity of the competition had peaked. This time, his victims got even: they all took hold of his car by the fenders and bounced it up and down, moving it as they did all the way back to the street — "leaving a shaken and subdued Kimball inside." In the animation department, Kelly worked on three Mickey Mouse shorts — *Clock Cleaners* (1937), *The Little Whirlwind* (1941), and *The Nifty Nineties* (1941). He worked with Kimball on the latter, and Kimball recalled some of the results:

Kelly did a whole sequence illustrating the song "Father, Dear Father, Come Home with Me Now" — a take-off on an old lantern-slide show. He drew a caricature of Lou Debney [an assistant producer who later worked on Disney's True Life Adventures] wearing a little girl's blond wig and singing the song. Every time the film cut to this little girl on stage singing, she'd be crying a little harder, until at the end she had a complete breakdown, sobbing and standing knee-deep in gushes of tears. It was so funny that Fred Moore and I fell down laughing when we saw it. But Walt [Disney] thought the in-joke and the little girl animation were gross and decided to cut them out (p. 136).

Kelly also worked on *Pinocchio* (the Lampwick sequence; released in 1940), *Fantasia* (1940), *The Reluctant Dragon* (1941), and *Dumbo* (1941). In *Dumbo*, he and Dave Swift, an assistant animator, were supervised by Kimball in animating the celebrated crow sequence in the film. The little elephant Dumbo is the object of ridicule in the circus of which he is a member because he has enormous ears. One night, he mistakenly imbibes some liquor, which has contaminated his drinking water, and gets drunk. The next morning, he awakens to find himself on a branch high up in a tree, surrounded by a half-dozen hip crows. The crows strut around, needling him and singing. Eventually, it develops that Dumbo got up into the tree by flying — using his ears as wings. The crows encourage him to try again with a few more choruses of their song, and by the end of the sequence, Dumbo is soaring through the air. Subsequently, he becomes the star of the circus, the celebrated flying elephant, thereby achieving not only

fame but acceptance.

In early April 1941, Kimball was given the sequence to animate, he said, because Disney had the idea that Kimball was "good at dancing and music stuff" (probably because he heard about the concerts in the john). And Kimball had done an animated take-off of Cab Calloway for the Silly Symphony *Woodland Cafe* in 1937. To hear him tell it, Kimball left the animation of the sequence almost entirely to Kelly and Swift:

I would draw the size of the figures, explain the business, and rough out a step or two. Kelly and the guys would bring in their test animation and put it on my Moviola, and without even getting up to look at the footage, I'd yell, "Cut it in!" We had a hell of a deadline; some of us were doing forty feet a week then, which was unheard of (p. 135).

Kelly and Kimball's love of old-time music is hilariously indulged in the sequence. In fact, as the crows strut their way off the "stage" in a classic walk-away, we listen to the closing chords and the crows' soft rhythmic murmurs ("chaa, chaa") and can almost hear them gently reverberating off the tiled floor and walls of the men's room down the narrow corridor from the animators' offices.

The sequence is significant to Kelly watchers for another reason: it may have been Kelly's first public display of his lifelong fascination with the dialects of the Southern United States. The Southern accent in this case was tinged with African-American overtones: the crows were black, after all. And their obvious racial identity eventually made trouble for the film. At first, according to Kimball, no one made any objection. "Uncle Tom stereotypes were part of our American scene [then]," he observed, citing Aunt Jemima as an example (to which we could add the chef for Cream of Wheat, and Jack Benny's manservant Rochester, as well as Stepin Fetchit and every rotund black maid in a Hollywood movie). To make the sequence sound au-

thentic, black singers had been hired to do the singing for the crows.

"When we did this sequence, nobody talked much about it," Kimball said. "But at the preview, it got a big hand, and then everyone realized that the scene of the crows teaching Dumbo to fly was one of the highlights of the film. We didn't get any racial protests until later with *Song of the South* [1946], which was picketed by the NAACP [presumably for the portrayal of Uncle Remus and his fellow plantation workers as wholly subservient].

From then on, *Dumbo* was kept on the shelf. "Because of the black crow sequence," Kimball went on, "the Studio was afraid to re-release the picture for years." But, he recalled, for the Montreal Film Expo in 1967, after Disney had died, the Canadian Film Board requested a copy of the film to show. Studio executives were nervous but finally sent the film. "So there I was in Montreal," Kimball said, "and they ran not the big live-action pictures that were winning awards at Cannes, but *Dumbo*. And it brought the house down. The whole place cheered when my crow sequence came on. I get goose bumps just thinking about it."

Kelly loved everything about the South, Kimball said. "If Edna Ferber's *Showboat* would come to town, or any show that had that old hokey southern stuff, he'd go to see it two or three times," he said. Then, in the usual Studio custom, Kelly would draw gag cartoons about the show, with his friends as characters in the production. "He'd cast Larry Clemmons [another animator] as the gambler — the city slicker, the fast-talker. I was always the captain of the boat. Fred would be the girl or blonde lady, and Kelly would take the part of the old colored retainer.

"He never talked in southern dialect," Kimball went on, "only wrote it. And he would remember all the lyr-

WHIRRRR WHIRRR WHIRRRR

ics from *Showboat* and use excerpts when he drew up a gag for us" (p. 139-40).

It has been speculated that Kelly acquired his affection for Southern dialect during his World War II military service in the Foreign Language Unit of the Armed Services Institute, for which he illustrated dictionaries. And perhaps that is so — although it is difficult to understand how a foreign language can foster interest in the Southern dialects of American English. But Kelly had acquired his affection for Southern lingo long before. According to his widow, Selby Kelly, "his father used to read him things like *Uncle Remus*, and he picked up a lot of the Southern accent and the 'fun talk' from his dad" (p. 197).

Kimball observed that at first Kelly's rendition of a Southern dialect was like a foreign language. "A lot of people wrote to editors [in the early days of the syndicated *Pogo*] and complained about this," Kimball said, "and as a result, Kelly simplified the language. His first dialogue was authentic, I guess — spelled the way he

thought the words sounded" (p. 138).

The result, Kelly's southern fried brand of the dialect, lent itself wonderfully to the sorts of syntactic mutations that created confusion and comedy among his characters. Like the duel between Hatrack the Moose and Pogo that opens this volume. Hatrack naturally picks horns as the weapon. Pogo, generously advised by Albert, assumes that the horns in question are musical instruments. And Howland Owl aids and abets the confusion by saying he'll give a "*blow by blow* account" of the affair; how else would one use a horn save by blowing on it?

Similarly, when Howland applies the "slide rule" to predict the weather (1/26), it has nothing to do with the calculating device engineers and mathematicians employ. And his notion of "nuclear physics" (3/13) is likewise eccentric. The strip abounds in examples of this kind of ludicrous locution.

In a strip in which a character can talk about those innocent rhymes of childhood as "nursery rinds" (12/13), we can scarcely be surprised to hear in the cast's rendition of that antique Christmas carol that Good King Winceslas has become Good King Sourkraut and that he looks out "on his feets uneven" instead of looking out upon the Feast of Stephen (12/21).

Christmas 1949 was not the first time Kelly assaulted his readers' risibilities with his perversions of traditional Christmas carols, but it was the first national exposure for these concoctions. He had inaugurated both "Good King Sourkraut" and "Deck Us All with Boston Charlie" the previous year in the *New York Star* (12/22). He even used the same gags, but when he brought them back in 1949, he got more mileage out of them: this year, he got two daily strips out of the gags (12/21 and 12/22) instead of one.

Of the many catch phrases that Kelly would introduce in the strip over the years, the "Boston Charlie" carol is perhaps the favorite (probably because it is repeated on an anyule basis). In an article he wrote for *The Atlantic Monthly* in 1963, Kelly discussed the risks involved in messing around with the season:

The attempt was to parody the use of carols, but even though this was a poke at the usage, it was chancy. Readers make mistakes sometimes and think you're making fun of something else

besides the real object. It's a risky business. So the choice of carol had to be rather cool. It was discovered finally that one of the few songs used as a carol that had no sacred connotations was "Deck the Halls with Boughs of Holly." A few of the Pogo *characters got together and did a straight parody of the sounds made when you sing the right words to the carol... This caught on with a number of elderly child minds, and finally children themselves. There was relief in it, and few feelings were bruised. Those who protested against this violation of all that was holy were told as gently as possible that the carol in question was one that was left over from the midwinter pre-Christian pagan rites celebrating the return of the long day in ancient Britain.*

Kelly produced additional choruses for the song at various intervals (including, even, a few stray lines that were parodies of his own parody), and eventually, there were six choruses in all (published in their entirety in *Pogo Files for Pogophiles* by Selby Daley Kelly and Steve Thompson; Spring Hollow Books, 1992).

In the reprinted strips at hand, we have evidence of other effects on Kelly of his youthful sojourn in California. The Disney Studio had initiated an education program for its animators, and Kelly surely profited from the training he presumably received. He was not, according to Kimball, a particularly good Disney animator: his style was too personal for the Mouse Factory. "He had difficulty adapting to the model sheets, which were usually designed by other artists," Kimball remembered. "He would always manage to change the drawing of the characters a little. He unconsciously drew them the way *Kelly* thought they ought to look. Maybe, in hindsight, we should have made *our* drawings look like *his*. He drew very funny Mickeys; but when his test animation was screened later, the notes would always read, 'Have Kelly clean these up and make sure they follow the model sheet.'"

But if Kelly didn't like copying the models devised by others, he nonetheless could profit from the art courses the animators took. Walt Disney had started these classes in about 1933. He had decided that the day of "stick figure" animation was over; no more rubber-hose arms and legs. In his cartoons henceforth, the creatures would look more realistic. He also abandoned slapstick comedy — the anything-for-a-gag approach. Instead, the gags had to be appropriate to the character and to the situation. His films would not be comic strips in motion, which is how many animation

studios viewed their products. With these objectives in mind, art classes were started in animator Art Babbitt's home in the evenings. Eventually, the program outgrew Babbitt's domestic facilities, and the Studio hired Don Graham, a teacher at Chouinard's Art Institute, to conduct the classes at the Studio.

Graham ran into trouble almost at once. He began by teaching in the classical mode: animators were asked to sketch from static models, and they objected, pointing out that their drawings were supposed to move. Disney agreed. And in a remarkable memorandum he wrote to Graham in December 1935, he outlined his philosophy of animation and launched a new era at the Studio and in animation generally. (This document, one of the most important in motion picture history, is reprinted in Shamus Culhane's autobiography; pp. 117-127). Disney urged Graham to develop ways to teach the animators how to *caricature action and life,* not to duplicate real action or real life. Moreover,

"we must picture with the action the feelings of those characters." He stressed the need to exaggerate: "In someone bending over, can we show the exaggeration in that action by showing how the pants pull up in the back to an exaggerated degree that becomes comical? Can we show how the coat stretches across the back and the sleeves pull up and the arms seem to shoot out as from a turtle neck as they shoot out of the sleeves?" For Disney, the entire body was a vehicle for revealing character and feelings.

Graham changed his classes. He emphasized caricature and motion. To encourage animators to capture the "feel" of action, he had live models move around the studio and then leave, and the animators were directed to sketch the models from memory, attempting to capture the *impression* of the movements they observed rather than to duplicate them in photographic detail. Under Graham's tutelage, animators also learned the importance of balance to a body in motion, the ways that folds in clothing are formed by anatomical stretch points, and how to give weight to their characters.

Hank Ketcham, who was at Disney when Kelly was there and worked with him, gives the "University of Walt Disney" as his alma mater in his autobiography. Kelly could doubtless say the same. His drawings give Pogo and his pals physical presence: when they sit on a log, we can feel the weight of their bodies (see 2/6, for instance). And his treatment of the characters imbued each of them with an individual personality (of which Porkypine and Seminole Sam are doubtless the most striking examples in this volume, but they merely begin the list; all of the critters in the strip are sharply individualized).

Kelly's graphic treatment reached maturity in the early months of 1950. His lines were fluid, flexing to give volume as well as weight to his figures. And his renditions of the individual characters achieved stylistic consistency: the rough edges and pointy elbows had been rubbed off, and the characters were rounder in consequence. And therefore cuter. Their appearance jelled during this six-month period: they would not change as much in appearance in the rest of the strip's run as they had in the past year.

While all this was taking place in Kelly's genial swampland, the world outside went blithely on its way, largely ignorant of events that cast shadows of the future. In February, Joseph R. McCarthy, the junior U.S.

Senator from Wisconsin, gave a Lincoln Day speech in Wheeling, West Virginia, and during the course of his otherwise forgettable remarks, he waved a sheet of paper at his audience, claiming that it bore the names of 205 employees of the State Department who were known communists. And in March, someone in the CIA wrote a brief for the Secretary of State, predicting that the North Korea Peoples Army would attack South Korea in June 1950.

The Cast

In our continuing effort to discover just exactly how many characters were in the strip's cast, here is a list of those introduced in this volume's run — in order of appearance. (With this listing, the total of named or otherwise "significant" cast members reaches 67. It took only a year to compile this score.)

Hatrack the Moose
Harold the Ground Squirrel
Maiden Ladybug
Churchmice (three nameless)
Snowy Egret
George Woodchuck
Miz Heron
Bunny Boy
Miz Crow
Beaman Crow (Miz Crow's son)
Clarence the Pet Caterpiggle
Alabaster the Crow from Alabam
Humbug
Miz Potato Bug
Downwind the Skunk
Etaoin Shrdlu the Bookworm (The name is a byword among printers. On old-time linotype machines, the "home row" of keys for the operator's fingers spelled "Etaoin [left hand] Shrdlu [right hand].")
Adam Family (waterbugs)
Bear in Beanie
Fred the Plant Lice
Miz Beaver
Boat-tailed Grackles (triplets)
Harold the Harbinger
Miz Grackle
Roger the Mouse
Pup Dog

POGO

by Walt Kelly

DEC 12, 1949

DEC 13, 1949

DEC 14, 1949

DEC 15, 1949

POGO

by
Walt Kelly

DEC 16, 1949

DEC 17, 1949

DEC 19, 1949

DEC 20, 1949

DEC 21,1949

DEC 22, 1949

DEC 23, 1949

DEC 24, 1949

6

POGO

by Walt Kelly

DEC 26, 1949

DEC 27, 1949

POGO

by Walt Kelly

DEC 28, 1949

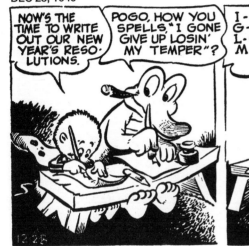

NOW'S THE TIME TO WRITE OUT OUR NEW YEAR'S RESOLUTIONS.

POGO, HOW YOU SPELLS, "I GONE GIVE UP LOSIN' MY TEMPER"?

I-G-O-N-E G-I-V-U-P- L-O-O-Z-N- M-Y-T-E-M-

I·G·N·G·V·P· L·O·Z·M·T...

P·E·R

AAARGH! YOU OL' TANGLE-DAGGERED, SNAGGLE-FANGED, BOB-WIRE-FISH-HOOKIN' OL' PEN, YOU!

HOW YOU SPELLS, "I GONE GIVE UP WRITIN' WITH PENS"?

DEC 29, 1949

HERE'S MY RESOLUTION FOR 1950..."GONE BE MORE CHEERFUL AND LESS FEARFUL..." HOW'S THAT?

OH, TOLERBOBBLE

MY PERSONAL ONES IS ALL WRIT OUT TOO, AN' IS LITTLE GEMS.

GOOD.. READ 'EM OUT --- I WILL WHISTLE AN' STOMP MY PERSONAL FEETS.

READ 'EM? MAN, I *WROTE* 'EM! LET'S SHARE THE WORK A LI'L BITTY --- *YOU* READ 'EM.

BESIDES, HOW MANY TALENTS YOU 'SPECT IS WROP UP IN ONE BOY? I ONLY GOOD AT WRITIN' AN' NEVER GIVES A HOOT FOR READIN' WHAT I WRITES.

DEC 30, 1949

DEC 31, 1949

POGO

by Walt Kelly

JAN 2, 1950

Panel 1: YOU'RE COVERED PRETTY WELL NOW MY FRIEND. WHEN YOU LIVE TO THE RIPE OLD AGE OF TEN OR MORE, YOU'LL BE ON EASY STREET.

DON'T LIKE STREETS - TOO NOISY.

Panel 2: BUYIN' ONE OF THESE U.S. SAVIN' BONDS IS THE BEST MOVE YOU EVER MADE

THE NEXT BEST MOVE I MADE WAS SHAKIN' THE DUST OF THE CITY FROM MY NATURAL BORN FEET.

Panel 3: PEOPLE KEPT SAYIN' 'LADY BUG, LADY BUG, FLY AWAY HOME --- YO' HOUSE IS AFIRE YO' CHILLUN WILL BURN!' -- NOT ONLY DIN'T SHE RHYME BUT SHE WAS DRIVIN' ME TO THE MAD-HOUSE --- SO OUT I CAME.

Panel 4: NEITHER FIRE NOR RUST NOR DARK OF NIGHT CAN CHANGE THE VALUE OF THAT BOND--- YOU IS SAFE, BUG, AND YO' CHILLUN IS SAFE.

CHILLUN! PLEASE, SIR. I IS THE MAIDEN TYPE OF LADY BUG, IF YOU DON'T MIND.

1·2·50

JAN 3, 1950

Panel 1: LI'L RACKETY COON, DON'T YOU WORRY 'BOUT LOSIN' YO' BOND OR HAVIN' IT STOLE --- OR BURNED UP--- U.S. SAVIN'S BONDS IS PROTECTED IN ALL WAYS.

YOU GOT ONE MY SIZE DUCK?

1-3

Panel 2: THESE ISN'T WEARIN' APPARELLELS PORKYPINE; YOU SITS ON ONE OF THESE BONDS FOR TEN YEARS AND YOU BE SOMEPLACE.

SHE DO SIT EASY---WHEN SHE GONE TAKE OFF?

Panel 3: WOULDN'T GET FAR IN TEN YEARS THO'---IT DIDN'T MOVE AN' INCH -- 'SIDES, IT LOOKS LIKE MY TICKET IS PUNCHED ALREADY.

PORKY, YOU IS CLOUDIN' THE ISSUE ---YOU KEEP THREE OF THESE BONDS FOR TEN YEARS AN' YOU'LL HAVE FOUR!

Panel 4: A COMFORTING LI'L THOUGHT, MAILMAN --- TWO IS COMPANY BUT THREE WILL MAKE A CROWD --- I'LL TAKE THREE.

WALT KELLY

10

POGO

by *Walt Kelly*

JAN 4, 1950

JAN 5, 1950

POGO

by Walt Kelly

JAN 6, 1950

SEMINOLE SAM, YOU OUGHT TO BE 'SHAMED TO SELL A DOG THAT BOTTLE OF WATER FOR ELIXIR.

WHAT'S WRONG WITH WATER?

1-6

DON'T BE HASTY, SON---- IF THAT DOG WAS A DUCK, HE'D BE SITTIN' PRETTY~--- DO YOU REALIZE WHAT KIND OF WATER THAT IS?

WET?

THAT'S *SUPERIOR* WATER --- THE VERY KIND THAT THE GOVERMINT USED WHEN THEY BUILT LAKE SUPERIOR --- HOW ABOUT BUYING A BOTTLE FOR THE FAMILY?

I DON'T GOT ANY--- YOU KEEP IT.

KEEP IT? HOW CRUEL -- HOW SELFISH ---ALL THE WORLD NEEDS THIS PRECIOUS FLUID-- HOW COULD I WITHHOLD IT--- WHAT COULD I DO WITH IT?

SOAK YOUR HEAD.

WALT KELLY

JAN 7, 1950

SHO', I'L GIVE YO' A RIDE, SEMINOLE SAM, BUT DON'T TRY TO SELL ME NONE OF THAT EE LIXIR; IT'S PLAIN WATER.

NOSSIR --HOWEVER, HOW'D YOU LIKE TO BUY A SLICE OF *TORONTO?*

NATCHEZ FLYER

1-7

TORONTO BELONGS TO *CANADA,* ALBERT

INCREDIBLE! AND I BOUGHT IT FROM SUCH A NICE OLD COUPLE IN FORT WORTH--SAID IT WAS IN THE STATE!

WELL, UNTIL I CAN CLEAR MY DEED, HOW ABOUT A SMALL FLASK OF *DRY WATER?* SEE, I POUR IT OUT AND MY HAND REMAINS DRY.

NO WONDER! THERE'S *NOTHIN'* IN THE BOTTLE!

THE NATC

NATURALLY -- I JUST EMPTIED IT IN THE DEMONSTRATION --- HOW'D YOU LIKE TO HAVE THE DRY WATER CONCESSION FOR THE *ATLANTIC OCEAN?* YOU COULD RUN OFF THE *WET* WATER, POUR IN THE *DRY* AND RENT THE BOTTOM OUT FOR A PARKIN' LOT.

OH, GOODY.

THE NATCHEZ FLYER

WALT KELLY

POGO

by Walt Kelly

JAN 9, 1950

COME ON AN' HELP ME POLE THROUGH THIS OL' SWAMP GRASS, SAM.

OOP! WE IS PUSHIN' THE OL' SCOW OUT FROM UNDERNEATH OF US! THE OL' POLE IS STUCK IN THE MUD.

WE'RE DOOMED! DOOMED! DOOMED TO SPEND THE REST OF OUR LIVES ON THIS POLE---- WE'LL SHRIVEL AND GENTLY FALL LIKE LOVELY AUTUMN LEAVES.

YOU IS MORE THE LOVELY HICK'RY NUT TYPE, DOCTOR.... SO STAY THERE 'TIL YOU RIPE. I GONE STROLL OVER TO THIS SWAMP ISLAND AND SET MY LOVELY SELF DOWN.

JAN 10, 1950

WELL, HERE WE ARE! MAROONED ON A DESERT ISLAND. WE'LL STARVE!

I WON'T STARVE.

MY FRIEND, I ADMIRE YOUR DEXTERITY CATCHING THAT FISH --- HOWEVER, IF I MAY MAKE A SUGGESTION, YOU USE MUCH TOO LONG A STICK TO BROIL IT.

MUCH TOO?

TOO MUCH TOO! MONSIEUR REYNARD, HEAD CHEF AT THE FRENCH BIBLIOTHÉQUE NATIONALE, TAUGHT ME THIS --- YOU CUT SO--- AND THEN YOU'RE ALL SET!

ALL SET?! FOR WHAT?

ALL SET TO TIE A STRING ON THAT STICK AND CATCH ANOTHER FISH.

POGO

by Walt Kelly

JAN 11, 1950

JAN 12, 1950

JAN 13, 1950

JAN 14, 1950

15

POGO

by Walt Kelly

JAN 16, 1950

Panel 1: HEY, POGO, A OL' *DRIVE* COLLECTOR COME PESTERIN' ME TODAY, BUT I DUCKED HIM! MAN, I SICK OF DRIVES COLLECTIN' FO' EV'RY THING. I SLIPPED OUT THE BACK WAY. *HAW-HAW!*

WHAT KIND DRIVE?

WE LEAVE ALBERT TEMPORARILY BESET BY THE CHURCH MICE

Panel 2: THE NATIONAL FOUNDATION FOR INFANTILE PARALYSIS. *HAW!* THEY CALLS IT A *MARCH OF DIMES!*

WELL, YOU PROB'LY WOULDN'T RUN INTO ANY LI'L CRIPPLE CHILD ANYWAYS.

Panel 3: AN' IN CASE YOU SEES ONE COMIN', YOU CAN SLIP OUT THE BACK DOOR AGAIN -- *HE* WON'T SEE *YOU* ---- BUT---

'COURSE --- YOU'LL SEE HIM.

JOIN THE MARCH OF DIMES
Fight Infantile Paralysis

Panel 4: *HURRY AND FIND THAT DRIVE COLLECTOR, BEAUREGARD. THIS PIGGY BANK IS GITT'N HEAVY!*

I'LL FIND HIM! I WANT TO SEE HIM MYSELF.

JAN 17, 1950

Panel 1: *HAW!* I SELLS OL' ALBERT TO THE CHURCHMICE. *HAW!* THEY THINK HE'S A OL' ABANDON' CHURCH ---- HEE HEE HEE!

Panel 2: POGO! IS YOU ALONE? *THEY IS AFTER ME!*

WHO? THE F.I.B.?

Panel 3: VOICES! I KEEP HEARIN' AND HEARIN' 'EM ---- BUT NOBODY IS AROUND!

MOVE OVER, FRED...

YEAH, GIVE ME SOME ROOM.

Panel 4: NO TRICKS NOW, ALBERT ~ I JES' WANT TO LIFT THE LID ---- AN' LOOK INSIDE --- HMMMM

HEY! WHO OPENED THE WINDOW?

HEY, POGO! STOP PEEKIN'!

Panel 5: YOU GONE HAFTA GET A CAT, SON ---- YOU IS GOT *MICE!*

PERSONAL MICE?

16

JAN 18, 1950

Panel 1: THESE MICE IN MY INNARDS *REEFUSE* TO GET OUT... ...WHAT I GONE DO? / OL' HOWLAN' OWL SAY HE GOT A TRAP WHAT WILL ROUSE 'EM.

Panel 2: AYE, FRIENDS, SCIENCE ALWAYS FINDS A WAY.

Panel 3: WOOooooOP! / SNAP!

Panel 4: LEMME *GO!* I'LL MURDER THE LITTLE BOUNDERS! THEY'VE *NO* RIGHT TO KEEP THE CHEESE! / PHOO! SOME CHEESE!

JAN 19, 1950

Panel 1: SCIENCE ALWAYS FINDS A WAY! PSYCHOLOWOGGY WILL ROUSE THEM LI'L OL' MICE OUTEN YO' INNARDS, ALBERT. / GOT AS MUCH RIGHT HERE AS ANYBODY. / ROGER! THAT'S ME.

Panel 2: I'VE TRAINED ROGER TO *DEECOY* THEM OUT. HE'LL TALK 'EM INTO LEAVIN'----- GO IT, ROGER!

Panel 3: HEY! IT'S ROGER! GREAT! NOW WE'VE GOT A FOURTH. CUT THE CARDS, CHARLES. / WHOSE DEAL?

Panel 4: DON'T FEEL BAD, OWL. IT'S BETTER'N THEM PLAYIN' HIDE AND SEEK.. *MAN!* ALL THAT OL' RUNNIN' AROUND! THEY GOT THE *COLDEST LITTLE FEET* THIS SIDE OF *LAPLAND!* / STILL, ROGER DISAPPOINTS ME.

JAN 20, 1950

JAN 21, 1950

JAN 23, 1950

JAN 24, 1950

POGO
by Walt Kelly

JAN 25, 1950

OL' ALBERT AN' POGO IS POKIN' FUN AT OUR WEATHER PROPHETEERIN'

HUMPH!

WE'LL SHOW 'EM -- MY CHART SHOWS: "POSSIBLE RAIN, **HOO**RICANES, FAIR, WARMER OR EARLY MORNING VOLCANOES."

WE'LL CONSULT THE INSTRUMENTS. **HEADS** SHE'S FAIR **TAILS** SHE'S RAIN.

WOOP! **WOOP!** A METEOROLOGIWOCKLE **CATASTROPHE**, DOCTOR OWL!

YEP, WE NOT GONE HAVE **ANY** WEATHER TOMORROW, **A-TALL**.

JAN 26, 1950

WE LOST THE APPARATUS SO WE ISN'T GONE FORE-CAST THE WEATHER TODAY.

BY JING! I WILL TAKE OFF'N SOME-BODY ELSE.

ALBERT'S RIGHT, OWL. IF YOU AN' CHURCHY IS IN THE WEATHER BUSINESS, YOU IS GOTTA DISH IT UP.

VERY WELL! WE SETTLES IT BY THE SLIDE RULE.

SLIDE AWAY, DOCTOR TURTLE.

RIGHT, DOCTOR OWL.

MAN! THE SLIDE RULE SHOW WE GONE GIT **SNOW**. *THAT'S* WHAT THE SLIDE RULE SHOW.

THAT WAS A GOOD SLIDE, DOC, --- AND THAT RULE IS A GOOD RULE.

JAN 30, 1950

COME! WE'LL FIND A **GROUND HOG!** HE'LL END OUR DILEMMA. THAT LI'L SAGACIOUS SEER WILL TELL US IF WINTER'S END IS AT HAND.

AND WHO CAN BEST FIND A GROUND HOG? WHO, INDEED, BUT MAN'S BEST FRIEND, THE NOBLE DOG. HE IS WISE AND KEEN OF MIND, ALERT AND READY, QUICK TO --- *WELL, HALLO!* HOW'D **YOU** LIKE TO HELP LOCATE A GROUND HOG?

GLAD TO! I'M A NATURAL BORN **WOOD-CHUNK** MYSELF.

GOOD FOR YOU!

A WOOD CHUNK!

THE DOG'S AMAZING MEMORY RECALLS A TIMELY VERSE: *HOW MUCH WOOD WOULD A WOOD CHUNK CHUNK WOULD A WOOD CHUNK CHUNK WOULD A WOOD CHUNK CHUNK WOODAWOOD WUNK CHUNK WOODA WOO WA WUH WOZZA HUM?*

GREAT! OR: HOW MUCH GROUND ROUND WOULD A HOUND DOG HOG IF A GROUND HOG WAS ROUND GROUND?

1-30

JAN 31, 1950

HERE'S A BONAFIDE GROUND HOG CAVE --- HEAR THAT SNORE?

ZZZZ

I'LL WAKE HIM GENTLE-LIKE. *"A BIRDIE WITH A YALLER BILL STOMP ALONG YOU' WINDEY SILL, HE SQUINT AN' SHINE HIS EYE AN' SAID, 'AIN'T YOU SHAMED, YOU SLEEPY HEAD?'"*

OOP! THAT VERSE WAS POSSIBLY A LITTLE LOW BROW.. LET ME TRY.

PFLAM!

"WAKE! FOR THE SUN, WHO SCATTERED INTO FLIGHT THE **STARS** BEFO' HIM FROM THE FIELD OF NIGHT, **DRIVES** NIGHT ALONG WITH THEM FROM HEAVEN AND **STRIKES** THE SULTAN'S TURRET WITH-- "

HOO BOY! STAND BACK!

OOP! THE SULTAN IS STRUCK ON THE TURRET WITH A 'LARM CLOCK.

PLOOP

"YESTERDAY, THIS DAY'S MADNESS, DID PREPARE.

HERE, NOW!

1-31

FEB 1, 1950

FEB 2, 1950

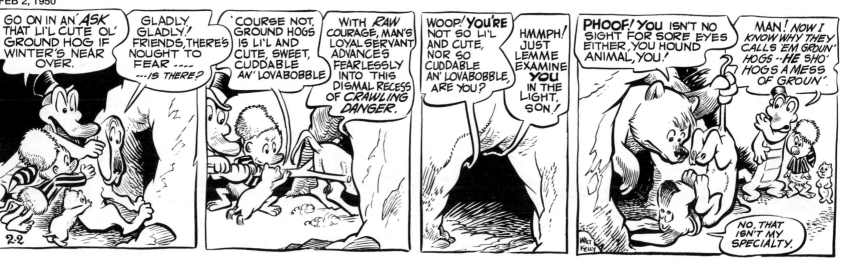

FEB 6, 1950

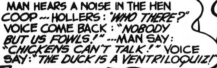

MAN HEARS A NOISE IN THE HEN COOP -- HOLLERS: *"WHO THERE?"* VOICE COME BACK: *"NOBODY BUT US FOWLS!"* -- MAN SAY: *"CHICKENS CAN'T TALK!"* VOICE SAY: *"THE DUCK IS A VENTRILOQUIZ!"*

HAW-HAW? MAN! YOU GOT NO SENSE OF HUMOR A-TALL? WELL, US CAN'T SPECT BLOOD OUTEN A STONE, CAN WE?

YOMF YOMF YOMF YOMF YOMF YOMF YOMF YOMF YOMF

YOMF? YOU IS *LAFFIN'!* PORKYPINE, YOU LIKES THAT OL' CHICKEN STORY! WHY, BLESS MY SOFT BROWN EYES!

NO -- BUT I THOUGHT THE ANECDOTE ABOUT GETTIN' *BLOOD* FROM A STONE WAS EXCELLENT HUMOROUS MATERIAL FOR SOME COMIC STRIP... MM -- MORE OFF TOPSIDE, CHURCHY.

COMIN' UP.

FEB 7, 1950

GONE TUNK MY NATURAL-BORN HEAD INSIDE AN' KETCH FORTY WINKS WHILE THE BARBER BUSINESS IS SLOW.

GUESS I'LL ASK UNCLE CHURCHY WHAT THIS IS.

OH... HOW HORRIBOBBLE! EE-YOWP!

MM?

SKEEEE - YOW!

WHUT GONE ON?

I DUNNO, MIZ HERON WAS SUDDEN TOOK HYSTER-ISICKLE.

POGO

by Walt Kelly

FEB 8, 1950

FEB 9, 1950

26

POGO

by Walt Kelly

I DON'T MIND IF YOU LOOKS AT MY BARBERIN' TOOLS, ALBERT, *BUT* DON'T CUT YOU'SELF ON MY RAZOR AN' *DULL* IT UP.

NAWP.

2-10

MAN, I BEEN ACHIN' *AN' ACHIN'* TO DRINK THIS OL' *DEE*-LICIOUS LOOKIN' DRINK.

HAW! HOW YOU LIKES *SHAVIN'* LATHER?

GUG!

THE *DRINK* WAS FINE, BUT SOME FUR-TAILED *VARMINT* SLIPPED IN AN' ALMOST CHOKED ME --- ---CAN'T YOU KEEP *CRITTURS* OUTEN THE SODY, TURTLE? 'TAINT FAIR TO THEM AS *PAR-TAKES* --- AN', NATURAL, 'TAINT FAIR TO THE CRITTUR

MY NATURAL BORN CAMEL HAIR SHAVIN' BRUSH!

ALBERT! YOU CAN'T GIT A HAIRCUT. YOU ISN'T GOT *NO HAIR NO HOW.*

I CAN GIT A *SHINE,* CAN'T I? SHINE 'EM UP, CHURCHY.

RIGHT

2-11

RAPPITY BAPPITY WHAP BAP-BAP PA-DOO

XOWP!

WOW! SOME HORRIBOBBLE VARMINT WAS PEEKIN' OVER MY SHOULDER.

KA-POW

27

FEB 15, 1950

FEB 16, 1950

FEB 17, 1950

FEB 18, 1950

30

FEB 20, 1950

SORRY TO DISTURB YOU DURIN' THE RUSH OF GITTIN' OUT THE SWAMP PAPER, POGO --- I GOT A *REE-*QUEST.

WHAT IT BE BUG?

I WANTS TO BE A **COPY-READER** --- LOOKY HOW I READS --- HERE'S A "B" OR MEBBE A "R", NEXT COME A "J" AN' THEN A --- WELL HMMM.

LOOK LIKE A PAST PARTISOOFLE WITH A SINGLE WING PLUS A DOUBLE "U" -- WHOLE THING SPELLS *"BAKIN' POWDER."*

BUG, KIN YOU *HUM?*

AT HUMMIN' I IS EVEN **MORE** WONDERFUL -- HMM-♩-MM HMMITTY-HM ♩ HMMMM HM-MM HMMM HMM HM M

I THOUGHT SO --- YOU IS A *HUMBUG.*

FEB 21, 1950

YEP, BEAUREGARD, THIS NEWSPAPER DO NEED A *CUB REPORTER*

THEN I'M THE MAN

WHY DOES YOU BRING YOUR OL' CLOTHES HAMPER?

THAT'S WHERE I FOUND HIM.

FOUND WHAT? YOWP!

CUTE, ISN'T HE? SOON AS I SAW HIM I DECIDED TO REPORT

GUESS YOU IS THE WRONG TYPE CUB --- MAYBE THEY WANTS **LION** CUB REPORTERS, OL' SWAMP KINDA LOW ON LIONS RIGHT NOW.

FEB 22, 1950

DON'T PASTE ANY OF THESE PICTURES OF WASHINGTON ON OUR PAPER UPSIDE DOWN.

IT HARD FOR ME TO TELL UPSIDE RIGHT ON THESE HUMAN TYPE FOLKS.

I BETTER DELIVER THESE BIRTHDAY NEWSPAPERS AFORE YOU GUMS 'EM UP.

US FOUND A BATCH OF CUTE LI'L PICTURES OF WASHINGTON THAT SOMEBODY LOST. SO WE STUCK 'EM ON OUR PAPER TODAY

HOW NICE.

'FRAID WE PUT 'EM ON KINDA SLOPPY----MAYBE TH' PAPER'S NOT WORTH THE PRICE, MIS' RACKETY-COON.

JES' YOU NEVER MIND, POGO----I KNOW YOU DOIN' YOUR BEST---WAIT, I GITS YOUR PENNY.

FEB 23, 1950

THERE YOU IS, MIS' POTATO BUG, OUR NEWSPAPER IS ONE YOU CAN READ WITH **FAITH** IN ITS **IN**·TEG·**GRITTY** AND **HOPE** FOR THE FUTURE.

I SEE SHE SAY IT GONE BE **FAIR** ALL DAY!

BOOM!

'COURSE, YOU GOTTA READ IT WITH A CERTAIN AMOUNT OF **CHARITY**, TOO.

POGO

by Walt Kelly

FEB 24, 1950

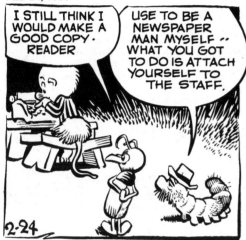

FEB 25, 1950

33

POGO

by Walt Kelly

FEB 27, 1950

FEB 28, 1950

34

POGO

by
Walt Kelly

MARCH 1, 1950

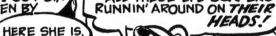

Panel 1: I'M A BUSY EDITOR, PORKYPINE, SO HURRY AN' SHOW ME YOUR NEW COMIC STRIP... I GOT SIX PENCILS TO SHARPEN BY FIVE O'CLOCK.

HERE SHE IS.

Panel 2: WELL, SAY! *HAW HAW!* THIS IS FUNNY AS A CRUTCH ---- ALL THESE LI'L SCAPERS RUNNIN' AROUND ON *THEIR HEADS!*

ON THEIR HEADS?

Panel 3: YOU IS HAD IT *UPSIDE WRONG,* CHIEF.'

OH ---- YES --- HMM -- WELL - UH -- HUM.

Panel 4: I DON'T GIT IT.

MARCH 2, 1950

Panel 1: PHOO · I QUIT! TRYIN' TO BE A COMIC STRIP ARTIST IS GOT ME DOWN.

DON'T GIVE UP! I'VE JUST INVENTED A SURE FIRE PRODUCTION METHOD.

Panel 2: FIE ON HIM IF HE WANTS TO QUIT ---- WE ISN'T LACKIN' TALENT --- SEE IF YOU CAN DRAW, CHURCHY LA FEMME.

NOTHIN' TO IT

Panel 3: SAW HER OFF, OWL, I IS READY TO START A NEW ONE.

MAN, YOU IS DRAWIN' AS FAST AS I IS SAWIN'.

Panel 4: LOOKY! IN A COUPLE MINUTES OF WORK WE IS GOT ENOUGH STRIPS FOR A MONTH.

LONG AS WE DOESN'T RUN OUT OF PLANK WE'LL MAKE A *MILLION DOLLARS.*

MARCH 3, 1950

MARCH 4, 1950

MARCH 6, 1950

H'LO, DOWNWIND --- HOW'D YOU LIKE TO WORK FOR OUR NEWSPAPER?

NOSSIR!

HAD A COUSIN WHAT WROTE A NEWSPAPER COLUMN AN' HE GOT SO TRIGGER HAPPY THAT HIS OWN FAMILY WASN'T SAFE --- HIS NAME WAS UPWIND OR EASTWIND OR ·· *W-- OOOP!*

ANYWAY, THAT BOY WAS MAD AT EVERYBODY --- WHY, HE COULDN'T GET WITHIN *ARM'S LENGTH* OF *HIMSELF* WITHOUT HOLDIN' HIS NOSE AN' COVERIN' HIS EYES.

MY SAKES-- DID *EVERYBODY* OBJECK TO THE POOR CRITTUR?

WELL, NO ---- SOME DIDN'T OBJECK -- BUT THEM AS DIDN'T WASN'T *REALLY* BREATHIN' NO HOW.

3-6

MARCH 7, 1950

GOOD EVENING, GENTLEMEN, I'D JOIN YOU FOR A BRIEF RONDELAY, BUT I'M ON MY WAY TO VISIT AN ACQUAINTANCE, AS IT HAPPENS, A *LADY.*

WHY. POR- Q- PINE!

OH, SHE'S NO *BEAUTY.* BUT SHE OWNS THE SQUEAKIEST SEE-SAW SOUTH OF SAINT LOUIS.

THE CATAMO

3-7

I TELL YOU, IT'S FAIR ELEGANT, SOARING HIGH INTO THE NIGHT AIR TO THE MUSIC OF AN UN-OILED SEE-SAW. THERE'S MAGIC IN IT, AND EXERCISE, GOOD FELLOWSHIP AND CULTURE. ALSO, WITH TEN FEET OF YELLOW PINE BETWEEN 'EM, A PAIR OF PORKYPINES CAN BE *MIGHTY* COMFORTABLE.

OL' PORKY GOT THE SAME TROUBLE IN HIS TRIBE AS I DO IN MINE --- SOME OF *MY* RELATIVES YOU CAN'T TOUCH WITH A TEN-FOOT POLE-CAT.

POGO

by Walt Kelly

MARCH 8, 1950

THIS IS POGO'S LI'L *PRINTIN' PRESS* -- SHUCKS, ANYBODY CAN WRITE FOR A NEWSPAPER IF THEY GOT A LI'L MACHINE WHAT SPELLS EVERYTHING.

NOTHIN' TO IT--- *WATCH!*

WOCK POCK

OOSH! MY *SCHNOZ!*

SOMEHOW I GOT A SHARP PAIN IN THE HEAD BONE AN' NOW EVERYTHING IS BLACK.

NEWSPAPER BUSINESS IS *DANGEREST* --- NO WONDER THEM LI'L *SPELLIN'* MACHINES GOT *SPOOLS OF BLACK BANDAGE* ALL HANDY.

EASY, FRED, EASY!

3-8

MARCH 9, 1950

GOOD AFTERNOON, YOUNG MAN, I'M A BOOKWORM BY TRADE, READY TO REVIEW A BOOK, RUN ERRANDS OR ANSWER THE TELEPHONE.

OL' ALBERT AN' POGO HAVE A NEWSPAPER ---- MIGHT BE THEY NEEDS A BOOK-REVIEWER

TAKE THIS BOOK I RIDE ON, ITS THE WRONG COLOR ---- AND CHEAP AT THAT. SEE, IT *RUNS!* DOESN'T RESIST WATER.

NOW THIS PAGE CHOSEN AT RANDOM IS *LUMPY* WITH PUNCTUATION --- *HARD* ON THE TEETH --CRAWLING WITH CONSONANTS ---- *UGH!* WHAT SHODDY MATERIAL!

AH, ME! MODERN LITERATURE HAS NO STAYING POWER! SEE, IT WENT DOWN LIKE A *STONE.*

WHAT WAS THE NAME OF THE *BOOK?*

OH, WHO KNOWS? I DIDN'T READ THAT FAR.

3-9

38

POGO, I GITTIN' TIRED OF THE NEWSPAPER BUSINESS --- SAY! LET ME TRY THAT!

NO WONDER YOU IS A GOOD SPELLER! YOU GOT A LI'L SPELLIN' MACHINE!

AAH! THIS BLACK-STAGGERED LI'L BLAGGARD IS SNAGGED MY FINGERBONE!

ARRGHFF! YOU BOG STOMPIN' TREECHEROUS LI'L SNEAK! YOU AMBUSHED ME! LEGGO! LEGGO!

WELL, ALBERT, THAT PUTS US OUT OF BUSINESS ALL RIGHT -- YOU IS SMASHED OUR ONLY PRESS TO BITS.

AN' NOT ANY TOO SOON! THE FREEDOM OF THAT PRESS GOT SO FAR OUT OF HAND WE MIGHT ALL OF BEEN CON-SOOMED!

HEY, POGO, COME AN' WATCH MY FRIEND, THE BOOKWORM, HE'S REVIEWIN' A BOOK FOR YOUR NEWSPAPER.

BUT, WE IS OUT OF BUSINESS.

IT'S JUST AS WELL --- THIS BOOK WILL NEVER GET BY -- ITS PACE IS ALL WRONG -- -- THE PLOT IS DISJOINTED- -- THE CHARACTERS ARE WEAK ITS SPELLING IS BAD!

YES, BAD SPELLING --- DON'T LOOK AT ME LIKE THAT, YOUNG MAN --- BAD SPELLING IS BAD SPELL-ING ------ WHAT'S THE NAME OF THIS BOOK, ANYWAY?

WHAT YOU SAY HIS NAME IS HOUN' DOG?

MR. SHRDLU- ETAOIN SHRDLU.

HMMM, WELL WELL!

MARH 13, 1950

MARCH 14, 1950

MARCH 15, 1950

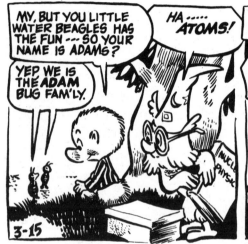

MARCH 16, 1950

41

MARCH 17, 1950

WHY'D YOU POP THE ADAM BUG FAM'LY INTO THAT BOX?

THEY IS THE ONLY LOOSE ATOMS I IS SEED -- I GONE MAKE A BOMB AN' BE A MILLIONAIRE.

BOMBS IS A PROBLEM, OWL; THEY IS NO GOOD.

NO -- THEY PUTS EVERYTHING TOO EVERYWHERE AN' IN LI'L BITS, TOO.

THAT'S THE ADVANTAGE OF THIS TYPE BOMB -- A ATOM BOMB CAN PUT EVERYTHING ALL OVER NOWHERE -- NOTHIN' TO SWEEP UP --

NO MUSS, EH?

ABSOLOOSELY NO MUSS ... SOLVES YOUR PROBLEM.

GLAD OF THAT, THO' IT'S NOT EGGS-ZACKLY THE PROBLEM I HAD IN MIND.

PSSST.. BUGS, YOU OKAY?

3-17

MARCH 18, 1950

WELL, I GLAD YOU IS FINALLY PUNCHIN' HOLES IN THAT BOX TO GIVE THEM ADAM BUGS SOME AIR.

FOOSH --- THIS HOLE IS FOR THE BOMB'S FUSE.

BOOK SAY: WHEN YOU SPLITS AN ATOM, IT ..

SPLITS A ADAM!? OWL, YOU ISN'T GONE USE THEM FRIENDLY BUGS FOR BAIT?

WHAT A IGNORAM-BUMPTIOUS YOUTH! BAIT IN-DEED! POGO, YOU JUS' DON'T UNDERSTAND 'BOUT FISSION A --TALL --

SO!

I KNOWS THIS MUCH 'BOUT FISHIN' OWL --- WHEN YOU USES A CRITTUR FOR BAIT, IT SORT OF SPOILS HIM FOR ANYTHING ELSE .. AN' I ISN'T GONE LET YOU DO IT TO THE OL' ADAM FAMILY.

WHY, POGO!

3-18

MARCH 20, 1950

THAT LOOK LIKE A *MIGHTY* SIZEABLE **LUNCH**, POGO --- ROOM FOR AT LEAST **TWO** ---

IT'S *NO LUNCH!* THESE IS THE ADAM BUGS I RESCUES FROM A FIEND WHAT WAS GONE USE 'EM FOR BAIT.

BAIT NOTHIN' -- POGO STOLE MY ADAMS OF WHOM I WAS GONE MAKE A BOMB OF.'

HAW! BAIT AN' *BOMBS,* INDEED! WHAT **BALDY.** DASH!

THINK I'LL JES' PLAIN FOLLOW POGO. I *KNOWS* A LUNCH BOX WHEN I *BE-HOLES* ONE.

YOU IS RUINED MY LIFE WORK, POGO --- NOW I GOTTA WALK CLEAR HOME FOR ANOTHER **BOX.**

AND, *MAN!* I IS *REALLY* GONE **PACK** THAT ONE!

HE SOUND LIKE THE BOY TO FOLLOW.

3-20

MARCH 21, 1950

POGO RUN BY WITH A LI'L BUNDLE AN' OWL HOLLER *HE* GONE PACK A *BIGGER* ONE --- THEM LI'L SCAMPS IS CARRYIN' *CONCEALED LUNCHES.*

OH, YOU *TENDER* LI'L THINGS!

TENDER LI'L THINGS! SOUNDS DEE-LICIOUS --- I IS GONE FIND **OWL** -- HE GONE HAVE A PLENTY OF THEM GOODIES.

OL' OWL WAS GONE USE US FOR BAIT? WELL, MEBBE HE WOULD OF SPLIT WITH US.

SPLIT *WITH* YOU? FOOP! HE WOULD OF SPLIT YOUR PERSONALITY *RIGHT* DOWN THE MIDDLE WITH A *BAIT* KNIFE.

BEIN' *BAIT* DON'T PAY --- IT **SPOILS** YOU --- EVEN DO YOU **KETCH** SOMETHIN'.

CAN'T WIN BEIN' BAIT, HUH?

NOPE, BAIT *NEVER* WIN.

3-21

MARCH 22, 1950

Panel 1: HEAR UNCLE POGO SAY USIN' A CRITTUR FOR BAIT SPOILS HIM --- WHAT HE **MEANS**, UNCLE PORKYPINE?

WELL, FISHIN' IS A CONTEST 'TWIX **YOU** AN' THE **FISH** ··

Panel 2: OL' **BAIT** IS YO' **AD**VANCE GUARD --- HE OUT THERE MANNIN' THE HOOK --- SOME-TIMES HE GIT NO ACTION A-**TALL** --- JUS' SLOGS 'ROUND GITTIN' ALL SOGGIED --- (DON'T HORSE 'EM IN, SON ··)

Panel 3: SOON HE'S FRIZZLED TO A FRAZZ --- HE NO GOOD FOR NOTHIN' --- HE'S ALL USED UP...

S'POSE HE **DO** GIT SOME ACTION MANNIN' THAT HOOK; WHAT IS HE **THEN**?

Panel 4: KA-PUT!

GESUNDHEIT!

3-22

MARCH 23, 1950

Panel 1: OL' OWL CLAIM HE MAKIN' A **ADAM BOMB** --- **HAW HAW** ~~ HE CAN'T PULL MY WOOL OVER THE ICE --- HE UP TO **SOMETHIN'**.

Panel 2: I B'LEEVE HE'S **PREE**PARIN' A BIG OL' **LUNCH** --- **HAW!** I WILL SPY OUT HIS SECRET -- HE'LL NEVER KNOW ME AS A OL' **SIZZLE GRINDER**.

Panel 3: DOG MY CATS! A HANDSOME MAN LOOKS GOOD IN ANYTHING --- I SHOULD OF BEEN A ACTOR -- MIGHT OF BEEN ANOTHER **RING-TING-TING** -- MY **DISGUISE** IS IMPENATRABOBBLE!

H'LO, LI'L FROG TADS.

Panel 4: H'LO, ALBERT --- YOU COTCH YO' HEAD IN A **GRACKLE** NEST?

3-23

44

MARCH 24, 1950

THERE GO TURTLE, UP TO OWL'S HOUSE. NOW I'LL SEE IF THEY IS TRYIN' TO HIDE SOME GOODIES.

3-24

CHURCHY, WE IS GONE MAKE A ADAM BOMB --- IT'S ALL THE RAGE ..... YOU ALL SET TO FIGGER, FELLOW-SINUS?

YEP, I BRINGS MY EE-RASER

NOW IF YOU SPLITS A ADAM BY DIVIDIN' HALF THE PARALLELO-GRAM CRACKIES WITH THE HIPPOPOTENUSE, YOU TURNS OFF THE **RADIO** ONTO THE ANGLEWORM OF THE ···

HOLD IT .... FELLOW-SINUS! HOLD IT, **BOY**!

MEBBE HIPPOPOTENEESE DON'T LIKE *GRAM CRACKIES* ---*BESIDES THEY IS FAT AN' SCAREY* AN' MIGHTY NIGH AS *FIERCER* NOR A *RHINOCER-WURST*.

RIGHT! I WILL *REE-*MOVE THE CENTER-FRUGALS

MARCH 25,1950

MAN SAY ONE TIME THAT ADAMS IS INDIVISIBLE ~ *HAW*..SCIENCE IS PROVED *OTHERWISE*.. TAKE A NOTE, CHURCHY.

3-25

FIRST: ADAMS IS *NOT IN-DIVISIBLE* ---MAINLY NAMELY CAUSE *I* IS SEED THE LI'L ADAM BUGS WITH MY OWN EAGLE-TYPE EYE BALLS, HARRUMPH!

HOW YOU SPELLS THAT "HARRUMPH"?

NOW, TO SEE IF THEY IS PACKIN' SAN'WICHES. THEY'LL NEVER KNOW ME DISGUISED AS A SIZZLE GRINDER.

HEY! SHARPEN 'EM UP TODAY?

YOWP! A FOREIGN POWER! EAT THE NOTES EAT THE NOTES.

POGO

MARCH 27, 1950

HOWDY, STRANGER. THE MISSUS SENT ME LOOKIN' FOR THE BORRY OF A CUP OF SUGAR.

DON'T LOOK AT *ME* --- OL' OWL AND TURTLE IS UPSTAIRS HOARDIN' EATIN'-FOOD *HANOVER* FEETS.

TAKE SOME MORE NOTES ON *ADAM* BOMBS, TURTLE.

WE IS RUN OUT OF BREAD AN' JAM FOR MAKIN' NOTES, SO I MAKES 'EM ON THE SAUCER.

GOOD! WE MIGHT EVEN MAKE A OL' *FLYIN'* SAUCER.

AHEM

I WOULD LIKE TO BORRY THE LOAN OF ..

YOWP! ANOTHER FOREIGN POWER! EAT THE NOTES AGAIN! *EAT THE NOTES!*

OOMF! TAKE THE SPOON OFF!

MARCH 28, 1950

SO THEY SLAM THE DOOR IN YO' FACE --- OH, I *KNOWS* THEY UP TO SOME SORT OF PRIVACY.

THEY IS UP THERE EATIN' GOODIES AN' WON'T GIVE ME THE BORRY OF A MEASLE CUP OF SUGAR.

NOW DR. TURTLE, YOU SEES A *GEE*-RANIUM PLANT AN' A LI'L BABY *YEW* TREE --- (IS THE DOOR LOCKED?) S'POSE I CROSSES THESE KIDS --- WHAT THEN?

I KNOWS! I KNOWS! YOU CROSSES 'EM AN' YOU GITS TO THE OTHER SIDE.

HOW *REE*-DICULOST! IF YOU CROSS THESE, *YOU GITS A YEW-RANIUM* BUSH!

HMMPH

WELL, DR. LYSENKO, *WE BEEN WAITIN'* HALF A HOUR --- MEBBE IF WE CROSSES OUR FINGERS, TOO?

POGO by Walt Kelly

MARCH 29, 1950

MARCH 30, 1950

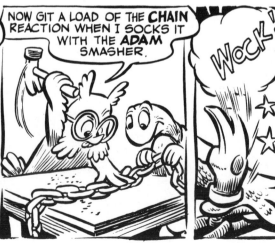

MARCH 31, 1950

YESSIR, FRIEND, I IS CONVINCED THAT OWL AN' TURTLE IS *HOARDIN'* A *TREE*-MOUNDOUS LUNCH AN' WON'T GIVE *US* ANY A-TALL!

ALL THEM NOTES I MADE IS SORTA HOM*OGE*NATED -- MOSTLY I GOT A MESS OF *"B"s* -- A FEW GRAVY SPECKLES AN' A COUPLE SAMMY COLONS.

"B's" HMM?

"*B*s" GIVE ME A *IDEA* --- C'MERE CAP'N LA FEMME.

HOLE OPEN THE BOX, SON --- *BEES* IS MIGHTY NIGH AS SMALL AS THE *ADAMS BUGS* AND THEY IS A PECK MORE *EX*PLOSIVE --- *WE GONE CONSTRUCT A "B" BOMB* 'STEAD OF A "A" BOMB.

3-31

APRIL 1, 1950

NOW WE IS *REALLY* GOT A BOMB --- A *BEE* BOMB WITH A WHOLE *BEE*-HIVE IN IT.

WE IS *LEADIN'* THE LEAGUE - I WILL HELP YOU DOWN THE LADDER, DOC.

YOWP!

AT LAST! WE CAPTURED THE LUNCH.

AND NOW, MR. SMART CATS, I IS GOT THE BIG OL' LUNCH AN' YOU CAN WATCH *ME* DEE-*VOUR* THE ----

NO --- *WAIT!*

LIKE THE MAN SAY, SON, *WAIT.*

I FIGGER IT BETTER TO *DEE-VIDE BEFORE* YO' *DEE-VOUR* --- RATHER 'N GO TO ALL THAT FUSS *AFTER* YOU EATS IT, BROWN EYES.

4-1

WALT KELLY

APRIL 3, 1950

APRIL 4, 1950

POGO
by Walt Kelly

WE SO BUSY HOSSIN' AROUND LAST COUPLE WEEKS THAT I ISN'T HAD NO TIME TO TELL YOU A STORY, LI'L RACK-ETY-COON CHILE, AND IT ALL REMINDS ME OF UNCLE WILLY WHAT HIRED A OL' ALLIGATOR TO PROTECT HIM ---

OTHER FOLKS GITS 'GATORS TOO --- SO WILLY HIRES A BIGGER ONE --- SO OTHERS HIRES A BIG-GEREST --- UNCLE WILLY GIT SERIOUS.

HE GIT HISSELF THE MOST TREE-MOUNDOUS 'GATOR IN THE WORLD -- AN' THAT 'GATOR DON'T MESS 'ROUND -- HE BUST OUT 'N' GOBBLE UP OL' WILLY JUST AS CLEAN AS A WEASEL.

SETTLES WILLY'S HASH, HUH?

YEP, IF YOU PROTECTS YOURSELF WITH THEM 'GATORS, SON ~ IT DON'T MAKE NO DIFFERENCE WHOSE 'GATOR EATS YOU

HEY! YOU IS SCARIN' ME!

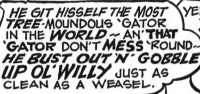

4-5

COURSE, YOU CAN POKE FUN AT US SCIENTIFIC MINDS DOES YOU WISH, BUT OUR METHODS IS THE WAYS OF THE FUTURE ~ WE MESS 'ROUND WITH THE ELEMENTS --- FINDS THE FRICTIONS ~ MAKES FRACTIONS OUTEN THE MASSES AN' NOO-TRALIZES THE ENERGY.

ALL THEM LETTERS ME AN' TURTLE WAS FIGGERIN' WITH IS IMPORTANT ~ MAN! WE RUNS THRU THE "A's" AND "B's" -- DUG ALL TH' WAY FROM H TO O -- BUT COULDN'T MINE OUR "P's" AND "O's" --- SO, THE COMMON COLD IS NOT ONLY UNCHECKED, IT'S UN-AMERICAN.

WE GOT UP TO "X", COULDN'T PROVE NOTHIN' AND LEFT IT 'TIL ANOTHER DAY --- SHOWIN' WHY "X" IS THE SYMBOL OF THE FUTURE --- AND YOU KNOWS WHAT "X" IS OF COURSE?

"X" IS THE UNKNOWN QUANDARY -- COME TOMORROW WE'LL SOLVE HER.

SPEAKIN' OF MULTI-PIE CATION, WHATEVER HAPPEN TO THE EASTER BUNNY?

THE ATLANTA BLOSSOM

4-6

APRIL 7, 1950

Panel 1: IT'S A CRY AN' SHAME··· OL' *EASTER BUNNY* IS *NOWHERE* ROUND ··· I WILL PERSONAL *DRESS* UP LIKE THE RABBIT IN A OL' *BUNNY* SUIT I WEARS ON COLD NIGHTS.
(sign: AL-BRT)

Panel 2: CAN'T JES' LEAVE THE CHILLUN GO WITHOUT *EASTER EGGS*··· *SAY,* WHERE DO THE OL' BUNNY *GIT* THEM EGGS?
STRONG OL' LEGEND SAY HE PLAIN LAYS 'EM PERSONAL.

Panel 4: POGO, SON, WHAT SIZE HAT YOU TAKES? I IS JUST HAD A *GREAT* IDEA.
OH, NO, YOU *ISN'T*·· I *IS* A MARSUPIAL BUT WHEN IT COME TO EASTER EGGS, I'M NOT ANY MORE SUPIAL THAN *YOU* IS!

APRIL 8, 1950

Panel 1: IS YOU SERIOUS THAT EASTER BUNNIES LAY THEIR OWN EGGS?
WELL, THE *BETTER* ONES DO ··· AND IF *YOU* GONE TAKE THE PLACE OF *OURS* ··· ····WHY··UH

Panel 2: BUT SOME EGGS GOT LI'L PINK DOO- HICKORIES ON 'EM ···FLOWERS··· LACEY BOWS··· EVEN *NAMES* ···· IN SUGAR..
WELL, I PREE- SUME THE OL' BUNNY TOOK A *COURSE* OR TWO AN'···

Panel 3: BUT YOU WILL *ADMIT* THAT'S QUITE A BIT TO 'SPECT FROM A *ALL*IGATOR?
DON'T TELL ME YOU IS S*T*UMPED BY ALL THAT NAME SPELLIN'?

Panel 4: 'TAINT THAT··· IT'S THEM EGGS WITH THE LI'L *WINDOWS* IN 'EM ··· HOW IS I GONE TO THINK UP ALL THEM LI'L *MELLERDRAMMERS* WHAT GOES ON INSIDE? I GONE NEED A FULL TIME *LIBRETTIST.*

51

APRIL 10, 1950

APRIL 11, 1950

APRIL 12, 1950

APRIL 13, 1950

POGO

by Walt Kelly

APRIL 14, 1950

APRIL 15, 1950

POGO

Walt Kelly

APRIL 17, 1950

APRIL 18, 1950

55

APRIL 19, 1950

APRIL 20, 1950

APRIL 21, 1950

Oh, Albert, how will I ever thank you for safe-guarding my own li'l' baby grackles which I mislaid when they was mere eggs?

Aw, shecks, Miz Grackle.

Enough of idle sentiment--- we'll never get all the bird watchin' done this spring if you all tarry hunk around passin' chit chat.

Well, the noble dog carries on ... alone ... unaided --- single-handed ---- hmmp ... what's goin' on?

AHA!

We is all DOG WATCHERS an' this is the first dog we ever watched -- now, students, take notes.

APRIL 22, 1950

How can I ever repay you for rescuing my li'l' grackle babies, dear friend?

AW 'twasnt anything ... any red blooded American alligator would of did the same.

I KNOW! We can be CROCODILE BIRDS like the plover of the Nile who plucks tid bits from the teeth of the smilin' crocodile.

Open wide, Albert. Us gone peck you clean as a weasel.

Careful, Miz Grackle, THAT is Albert's TONGUE.

What a pity ... it's such a BIG piece.

PLUCK EASY you li'l' dental hyenas.

57

APRIL 24, 1950

APRIL 25, 1950

POGO

by Walt Kelly

APRIL 26, 1950

ROGER! ROGER, THE MOUSE! GOSH, WE HAD A NUMBER OF LETTERS ASKING WHAT HAPPENED AFTER ALBERT SWALLOWED YOU WITH THE CHURCHMICE.

OH, I LEFT EARLY.

I WAS AHEAD IN THE PINOCHLE GAME--- RIGHT NOW I'M GOIN' TO A *MOUSE* CONVENTION. *THE MICE* OF THE *WORLD* ARE MEETING TO INVENT A *WORSER* MOUSE TRAP.

A WORSER MOUSE TRAP! WELL, IT'S *BEST* TO INVENT SOMETHING THAT DOESN'T WORK --- SUCCESS IS TOO RISKY TODAY.

YES, SUCCESS IS DANGEROUS.. *BUILD A BETTER MOUSETRAP TODAY* AND THE WORLD WILL BEAT YOU INTO A *PSYCHOPATH* BEFORE YOU CAN REACH THE DOOR.

WHEE!

APRIL 27, 1950

HEY, ALBERT, THE MICE ARE HOLDIN' A CONVENTION.

A *DULLER* PIECE OF INTELLIGENCE HAS NOT COME MY WAY SINCE CHRISTMAS, 1936.

DON'T LIKE CONVEN-TIONS?

NOR MICE! I CAN GIT ALONG WITHOUT BOTH.

THEY IS GOT A BIG CONVENTION HALL AND IT'S *FULL* OF GOOD THINGS TO EAT! WISH'T I WAS A MOUSE!

WHY, SOME OF MY BEST FRIENDS ARE *MICE!* RECKON THERE'LL BE ROOM FOR A BLOOD COUSIN LIKE ME ----- WHICH WAY TO *OUR* CONVENTION HALL, SON?

THE BATON ROUGE CANNON BALL

59

APRIL 28, 1950

Panel 1: IF WE SITS HERE ADMIRIN' THE PARADE MEBBE ONE OF 'EM WILL INVITE *US* TO THE CONVENTION HALL WHERE THE FOOD IS. / I STILL THINK YOU GOTTA *BE* A MOUSE. *PERSONAL.* / MOUSE CONVENTION WORLD MICE / DOWN WITH CATS

Panel 2: THE MEMPHIS MICE PROTECTIVE LEAGUE

Panel 3: ALL MICE WHAT MARCHES IN THE PARADE IS S'POSED TO GIT *EXTRA* CHONKLIT CAKE. / MICE OF NEW ORLEANS

Panel 4: FORT MUDGE DIVISION / SQUEAK! SQUEAK!

4-28

APRIL 29, 1950

Panel 1: IT'S NO USE, ALBERT! THESE MICE WON'T BELIEVE YOU'RE A MOUSE FROM FORT MUDGE / WHY NOT? / WELCOME WORLD MICE / MOUSE CONVENTION HERE / FORT MUDGE DIVISION / FREE FOOD FOR MICE

Panel 2: PHOO! NOT ONLY IS YOU TOO *BIG* TO BE A MOUSE --- YOU IS TOO UGLY --- STAY OUT! / FORT MUDGE DIVISION / SLAM

Panel 3: AAAH--*I* WOULDN'T GO IN THAT *MANGY* GOAT CAVE ANYWAY! IT WOULD BE A DISGRACE TO A RED BLOODED AMERICAN ALLIGATOR. / HER / ALBERT

Panel 4: 'CORDIN' TO THIS SIGN THAT THEM MICE SHUCKED OFF THE DOOR, THAT MANGY GOAT CAVE IS *YOUR* HOUSE! / WHAT? / ALBERT

4-29

WALT KELLY

MAY 1, 1950

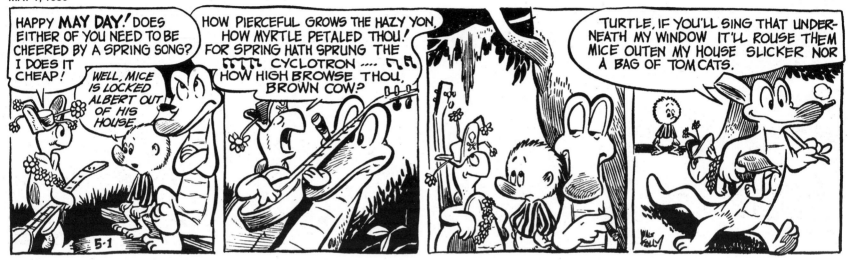

MAY 2, 1950

POGO

by Walt Kelly

MAY 3, 1950

THE DOG, MAN'S BEST FRIEND, MIGHT ROUSE THOSE MICE FROM ALBERT'S HOUSE --- THE DOG IS FEARLESS, QUICK OF MIND AND, AS YOU WELL KNOW, *REE* SOURCEFUL.

5-3

MM--- H'LO, SAM.

THE DOG IS ALERT.

YOU USE TOO LONG A STICK TO COOK WITH, POGO.

THERE! A LITTLE LESSON IN THE CULINARY ART..... *NOW YOU'RE ALL SET!*

ALL SET? FOR *WHAT?*

THE DOG IS A GENEROUS ADVERSARY.

YOU'RE ALL SET TO TIE A STRING ON *YOUR* HALF OF THE STICK AND CATCH ANOTHER FI ---- *FAUGH! YOU BURGLAR!*

THE DOG IS WILLING TO SHARE.

MAY 4, 1950

PLAY DEAD! DEAD DOG! GOOD! AH, WHAT A SPLENDID BEAST..... RELAX, SIR ---- LET LOOSE THE FISH! COME -- DEAD DOG! PLAY DEAD, SIRRAH-- *RELAX!*

HE GOT A DEATH GRIP.

5-4

WELL, LET'S SEE YOU RETRIEVE A FALLEN GAME BIRD --- *FETCH! FETCH, LAD, FETCH, I SAY!*

OH, HE'S A REGULAR 150 DOLLAR HOUND.

NOW THEN, SIR, SOFTLY PLACE THE QUARRY IN THE MASTER'S HAND WITH A FEATHER TOUCH.

ANY OTHER COMMANDS, MASTER? ANY OTHER SMALL DEMONSTRATION OF THE DOG'S TRULY GREAT ABILITY?

YES --- DROP DEAD AGAIN!

MAY 5, 1950

FOR A FEE I COULD TEACH YOUR FRIEND ALBERT HOW TO ACT LIKE A MOUSE ---- THEN THOSE MICE WOULD LET HIM INTO HIS OWN HOUSE.

LIKE THIS ---- YOU WOULDN'T KNOW ME FROM A *REAL* MOUSE, WOULD YOU? BE *HONEST NOW* ---- SQUEAK! SQUEAK!

SQUEAK! SQUEAKIE SQUEAK SQUEAK SKA-WEEK!

SQUEAKITY SQUEAK SQUEAK SQUEAK SQUEAK

YOWP!

SQUINK!

GLOONK

MAY 6, 1950

YOU, TOO, CAN BE A SUCCESS! TRAIN *NOW* FOR A CAREER THAT ALWAYS HAS AN OPENING!

WHAT SORT OF AN OPENING?

AN OPENING INTO THE *BEST* HOMES ----- AH, WHAT LITTLE ARTISTS ARE ALWAYS SLEEK, WELL FED, SHELTERED --? STEP A *LIT*-TLE CLOSER, FRIENDS, I'LL TELL YOU WHAT YOU SHOULD BE ...

WHAT? WHAT?

MICE

WHAT DID *YOU* HEAR?

MICE.

HUT-TUT-TUT TUT-TUT-TUT-TUT SHOOOOSH! GOOD JUMPING GRANDFATHERS! DON'T LET IT GET AROUND!

POGO
by Walt Kelly

MAY 10, 1950

MAY 11, 1950

MAY 12, 1950

MAY 13, 1950

HOO! HOO! TEACHER, I ISN'T LEARNIN' MUCH *MORE* ABOUT BEIN' A MOUSE --- I ALREADY IS PERFECK AT SQUEAKIN' AN' CREEPIN'

WHAT NEXT FOR A STARVIN' MOUSE-PUPIL, TEACHER? MEBBE A CRACK AT SOME LUNCH?

YES, MY FINE LITTLE MAN, **YOU** MAY LICK UP MY **CRUMBS**.

AND **YOU**, GOOD LITTLE ALBERT, **YOU** CAN PRACTICE GNAWIN' YOUR LITTLE WAY INTO THE HOUSE FROM WITHOUT.

FROM WITH-OUT **LUNCH**? I IS HUNGRY, TOO.

THE RUDIMENTS OF MOUSERY DO NOT INCLUDE BEIN' RUDE TO TEACHER --- *DIG* MY BOY, *DIG*!

SCHOOL FOR MICE

MY SAKES, I WOULD OF SWORE THIS WAS **MY** HOUSE WHEN I GOT UP THIS MORNIN'.

ALBERT, HOW IN THE WORLD IS A SCHOOL GET HERE? MUST IS IT'S A ACADEMY FOR **VETERANS**. THEY SPRINGS UP SUDDEN LIKE.

SQUEAK SQUEAK.

WELL, I IS A VETERAN **STUDENT**.....TEACHER SAY "*DIG A HOLE IN*," BEIN' A MOUSE ISN'T SO CUTE AN' BRIGHT EYED AS IT LOOK.

OH, I IS GREAT FOR GIVIN' VETERANS A HAND.

BY JING, THIS *IS* **MY** HOUSE!

ALBERT! YOU IS GNAWED IN! AND YOU EVEN *LOOKS* MORE LIKE A **MOUSE**!

POGO

by Walt Kelly

MAY 17, 1950

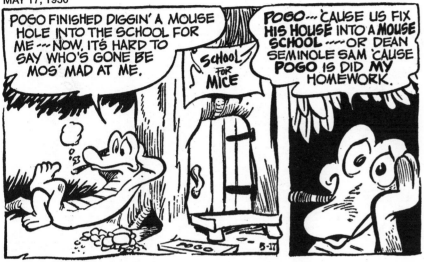

POGO FINISHED DIGGIN' A MOUSE HOLE INTO THE SCHOOL FOR ME --- NOW, IT'S HARD TO SAY WHO'S GONE BE MOS' MAD AT ME.

School FOR MICE

POGO --- 'CAUSE US FIX HIS HOUSE INTO A MOUSE SCHOOL ---- OR DEAN SEMINOLE SAM 'CAUSE POGO IS DID MY HOMEWORK.

BE-HOLE, STUDENT! ALBERT IS GNAWED IN AND EVEN GOT *MORE* OF A RATTY LOOK --- IF POSSIBLE.

OH, SQUEAK.

YEP. EVEN MY ALLIGATOR TAIL-BONE IS SKINNIED OFF TO A MORE *MOUSEY* SIZE.

MY COURSE IS A-MAZIN'! (SPECIALLY TO *ME*.)

IS *I* GONE LOOK LIKE *HIM*?

MAY 18, 1950

TEACHER, YOU IS TAUGHT ME TO BE SUCH A GOOD LI'L' MOUSE THAT MY LI'L' PINK NOSE CAN SMELL OUT *MOUSE* SPECIALTIES!

LET'S NOT CROWD THE FACULTY.

YOU IS GOT A FACULTY FOR BEIN' CROWDY YOU OWN SELF

ONE SIDE, PUPIL! AN' MAKE IT *SNAPPY*!

LITTLE GIANT BRAND "GOOD for MICE"

SNAP! SNAP! SNAPPITY SNAP SNAP SNOP!

SNOP?

LITTLE GIANT BRAND "GOOD for MICE"

MAY 19, 1950

MAY 20, 1950

MAY 22, 1950

ALSO AVAILABLE:

POGO

VOLUME ONE AND TWO

JUST WRITE TO:

FANTAGRAPHICS BOOKS

7563 LAKE CITY WAY NE
SEATTLE, WA 98117

70